# Katie

## The Young Life of
## Mother Katharine Drexel

by Claire Jordan Mohan

YOUNG SPARROW PRESS

P.O. Box 265 • Worcester, PA 19490

(215) 997-0791

Mohan, Claire Jordan
    KATIE: The Young Life of Mother Katharine Drexel

SUMMARY: Describes the young life of Katharine Drexel, a wealthy Philadelphia heiress, who surprised the world when she gave up her wealth to serve God and devote her life to supporting and caring for Native and African Americans. It reveals the events in her young life that led her to found the Sisters of the Blessed Sacrament whose mission was to serve these peoples at a time when their plight was largely ignored.

© Copyright 2001
Young Sparrow Press, Box 265, Worcester, PA 19490
(215) 997-0791, Fax (215) 997-5687
Printed in the United States of America.
First Printing.

ISBN #0-9621500-2-9          $8.95 paperback

M.K.D. photos: Sisters of the Blessed Sacrament, 1663 Bristol Pike, Bensalem, PA 19020
Photo Amanda Wall: John and Constance Wall
Cover Design: Carrie Gamble
Cover Portrait: Audrey Swanson Marlow, P.S.A., 1990

# Contents

To Jack, Jeanette, and Amy Wall

*"I rescue all who cling to me,*
*I protect whoever knows my name,*
*I answer everyone who invokes me,*
*I am with them when they are in trouble."*

— Psalm 91:10-13

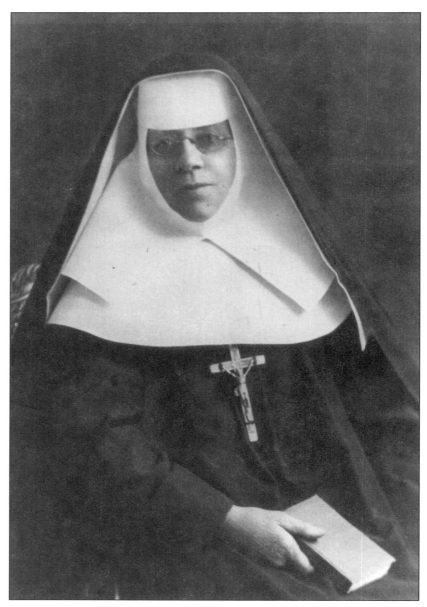

*Mother Katharine Drexel*

He never contemplated
our being alone
on the mountain.

He would not have brought us
into such difficult passes
if He had not meant to come Himself
to help us through them.
Then let us adore Him
by bravely going forth and
keeping our appointments.

He will be there.

Mother Katharine Drexel

*Hannah Longstroth*

*Francis Drexel*

# Prologue

The harsh clang of the door knocker startled us. Not that we hadn't heard it many times in the last few days. Yet this time, as we sat close together in the little sitting room at the top of the stairs, it seemed ominous. I don't know why I jumped. Did I have the feeling even then that it would signal a major change in my future life? Three girls, orphaned only days before by the sudden death of our darling father, we wanted to just sit there and talk about our papa and mama. There had been many condolence visits the last days from our relatives and friends, but now it was quiet. We were happy to be alone, though the big house seemed so empty to us now.

It was a gray February evening in Philadelphia. The clouds overhead promised snow overnight and already there was moisture on the ground. It was a night to stay indoors close by the fire. Our brownstone house was secured for the night. No one was expected. But the knocker had signaled and a few minutes later, our faithful butler came up the long stairs, and arrived in the doorway with a message.

"Two gentlemen priests downstairs to see the Misses Drexel."

Elizabeth, Louise, and I looked at each other.

"Kate, you go down," said Louise.

Our father's death had been a great shock to us. And barely two years ago our mother had died from cancer. It was so hard on us girls for they were the dearest parents you could find anywhere. Now our tears had dried. There was no more weeping, but our papa was gone, our mama was gone, and our hearts were gone with them.

We had been greeting so many visitors the last few days. Since this tired us, we had decided to take turns. We were not expecting anyone at this hour, but I didn't mind. Our mother had always taught us to be gracious and kind.

"Okay, Louise, this shouldn't take long. I'll be right back and tell you and Lizzie who they are and what they want," I replied.

I placed the long letter I had been reading on the table and quickly arose from the flowered chair. Lizzie and Louise stayed close to each other on the green velvet sofa facing the fireplace. The marble mantel clock rang seven times.

Pushing a stray curl off my forehead and carefully lifting my long black skirt, I left the room and walked slowly down the curving staircase to the hall below. I stared at the sparkling candle-lit chandelier and momentarily remembered many parties and dinners that we shared such a short time ago. I could hear the gaiety and laughter that had filled that hall as mama and papa had entertained. I could still see the women dressed in beautiful gowns, tiaras in their hair, and the men in their formal suits and bright cummerbunds. Would we ever be happy again?

I squeezed my eyelids tightly together to hold back the tears threatening to race down my cheeks. I couldn't go into that room crying. I straightened my shoulders and walked toward the dark parlor where the heavy velvet drapes were still closed in mourning. I wondered who these unknown priests were and why they were here. Through the arched doorway, I noticed two dark-haired men talking quietly as they sat, a little ill-at-ease on high-backed chairs near the window. They appeared to be consulting with each other, while sifting through papers in a stuffed portfolio which they had placed on the desk between them. They rose and bowed as I entered.

"Miss Drexel, I am the Director of the Bureau of Catholic Indian Missions," said the taller one as he reached out his hand.

"Indian Missions?" I asked cautiously as I released my hand from his strong grip and sat on the couch. Strangely, just last week I had read a book about the American Indians in the United States. It was titled *"A Century of Dishonor."* I didn't realize it then but before long those two words would be a part of my very own vocabulary.

The Drexel girls, our parents, the Indians — I can't go on with my story till you know us. I think I should tell you all about our family.

*Elizabeth Drexel at six years and*
*Kate Drexel at three years.*

# Chapter 1

# Our Family

The first thing you would notice about our family is how close we are to each other. We were raised by a wonderful mother and father with great affection and every material advantage you could imagine. And so the story goes like something in one of those fairy tales we all read when we were little. You know the kind I mean — the lovely princess, the handsome prince.

Once upon a time... (isn't that how fairy stories begin?) a beautiful lady named Hannah married a charming and wealthy banker named Francis. It was September 28, 1854. They were very happy and soon God blessed them with a beautiful daughter they named Elizabeth. She was the joy of their life for three years. Then one day Hannah became very ill and had to stay in bed for many weeks. While she was sick, another little girl was born to them. It was November 26, 1858. They called me Katharine Mary and my parents were both very excited at having two little girls to love. But the beautiful lady never got well. When I was only five weeks old, she died. I was told my papa was devastated, but I was too young to know or care. During my first years, my Uncle Anthony's wife, my Aunt Ellen, took care of all my needs — fed me my bottles, and best of all, cuddled me when

I cried. I was a happy baby!

Two years later Francis recovered from his grief, and found love again. Her name was Emma. On a lovely spring day in April 1860 they married in a flower-filled church surrounded by their many friends and relatives. It was at Old St. Joseph's Church in Philadelphia. I have been told many carriages carried the guests to the church where a specially selected orchestra and choir supplied the music, but I was too little to notice.

Shortly after the wedding day, the newlyweds boarded a ship for Europe. The trip lasted about five months and to two little girls, whose papa had always been nearby, it seemed like they were gone forever! When they returned in autumn a new life began for all of us. Now we had a mother of our own and joyfully we went to live in a beautiful brownstone house on a tree lined street in downtown Philadelphia. Our home was filled with everything you could imagine to make it comfortable and beauty-filled. We had lots of rooms, including a library, and a sweet little chapel filled with statues and religious paintings. We often prayed there alone by day. At bedtime, Papa would light the candles and Lizzie and I would hold our rosaries in tiny hands and say the beads along with our parents.

How fortunate we were in having Emma as our mother! She gave her heart to all of us and it wasn't until I was 13 that I learned she was not my birth mother.

It came about quite naturally, I remember one day while we were playing with our cousins at

Grandmother Langstroth's house, I called her aside.

"What is the matter, Katie?" she asked, "You look so serious."

We went into the living room away from the others and I sat down next to her on the sofa. The sun shone through the arched windows lifting my spirits as I searched for words to ask her a question that would move me for a bit into darkness.

"Grandmama," I asked, "why do Lizzie and I have three sets of grandparents? All the other cousins have only two."

She put her arms around me. "Katie, dear, I have something to tell you."

I noticed her eyes were moist — and then she told me the story of my birth. Tears filled my eyes, too and I began to shake as she spoke. Grandmother hugged me and her loving embrace made me feel safe. Perhaps it would have been better to have always known, but then many secrets were kept from children in those days. Emma was my mother and I loved her as much as ever, yet there was a feeling of sadness in my heart that never went away for the mother I never knew.

But back to my story...

Soon after the wedding, Papa bought a summer home for us on three acres of farm land in the country near a little village called Nicetown. It was a wonderful place. I think back now to all the good times we had as we climbed the ladder to the hayloft. We reveled in its sweet fragrance as we bounced around, tossing bits of hay at each other and giggling. Squealing with delight, we would swing on ropes that papa had hung from the trees, and race around the grassy meadow chasing each other.

We even had a donkey cart. It was so much fun! Lizzie and I would sometimes be allowed to hold the reins as we would drive into town to buy kerosene at the general store. Every day was the same routine.

"Good morning, young ladies," old Mr. Cutter greeted us as he put down his pipe and stepped up from his rickety rocking chair. "What can I do for you today? Would you like a lemon stick?"

"Oh, no thank you, Sir, we don't eat candy, just some kerosene, please," I answered.

You see, life was different in those days. Country homes had no electricity or gas for heat or light and no spigots pouring forth water. We read by the light of candles or kerosene lamps. We pumped cool water from the well outside the house, splashing it on our faces to cool us on the hot days and heating pails of it on the cast iron range to bathe in the evening.

By day we would tread carefully near the swamps to pick sticks of punk and at dusk, we would sit on the porch and burn it to keep the mosquitoes away. Mama read to us each night, then we would pray together before we were tucked into our cozy beds where we were lured to sleep by the sweet sounds of crickets singing outside our windows.

Each morning we would wake to the rooster's call. It was wonderful to lie there and savor the fresh scent of morning, blowing in through the windows and listen to the chirping birds.

"Elizabeth, Katharine, come now. Time to get up."

"Yes, mama," together we answered as the delicious aroma of hot cocoa and oatmeal called us from our beds.

After morning prayers and breakfast, papa would lift us from our chairs in his strong arms and swing us around.

"Come, little ones, papa must go to work. Walk with me to the station. I must catch the 8:05 train to Philadelphia."

On the way back, Mama would hold our hands and tell us the names of the wild flowers we were picking — daisies, Queen Anne's lace, black-eyed Susans, and golden rod — and talk to us about the wonders of God's creation. Some days we carried little baskets and along the way would stoop to pick blackberries or raspberries for supper. Mama would go back to the house to wash the berries or arrange our bouquets in tall vases on the hall table to please papa when he came home.

Other days we would dart around and play games of hide and seek in the tall grasses or take off our shoes and run down to the little creek which threaded its way through our backyard. There we would hop from rock to rock in the icy water. Oh, those were happy days! The air smelled of clover and birds sang everywhere!

*The three Drexel girls as children.*

# Chapter 2

# A New Sister

I will never forget an October night in 1863. An orange moon hung overhead and the sky was full of stars as we peeked out the bedroom window while we waited for our mama and papa to come to kiss us goodnight. We were living in our country home in Nicetown then and we were very tired from our outdoor play. I was having a hard time keeping my eyes open and Lizzie was sleepy, too. I hugged my baby doll and put her into bed next to me. Mama had just bought her a new wardrobe of clothes and that night I had dressed her in a pretty flowered nightgown. Finally, papa came to our room, but he was alone.

"Where's my mama?" I asked worriedly as I remembered she had been sitting in a rocking chair on the porch much of the day.

"She isn't feeling well, but don't worry, little ones, she'll be fine tomorrow," Papa answered as we all knelt by the bed and asked for God's blessings. Strangely, I still remember Papa had added "especially for mama tonight." Still, a few minutes later we were fast asleep.

The next morning was October 2. The sun was already up and birds were chirping in the tall tree outside our window as we awakened. Lizzie and I had barely opened our eyes when a smiling nurse walked into our room. She sat on our bed and held our hands.

"Guess what?" she said. "The angels were here last night, and they brought mama and papa and you a little baby girl."

"A baby sister!" we squealed as we jumped from the bed and ran to mama's room.

Mama still looked tired, but she gathered us close. She lifted a little pink blanket and showed us a tiny baby with blonde curly hair dressed in one of my doll's dresses. She explained that the angels had brought little Louise before she was expected and she didn't have any clothes to wear.

"You don't mind, do you?" she questioned me.

"Oh no, Mama," I answered as I nuzzled my new little sister, "I love this sweet little baby."

I carefully touched a tiny hand and kept my face close to hers. Little blue eyes opened to peek at me.

"Louise, baby, these are your big sisters," mama told her. "Say hello to Lizzie and Katie."

She whimpered her answer and Lizzie and I sat on the coverlet to kiss and snuggle close to our mother.

She was my little sister every day of my life. From the time she could toddle, her chubby hand was always reaching out for mine and she would follow wherever I went! Since she was born on the feast of the Guardian Angels, we called her our little angel. Now there were three little girls for mama to love — and we knew we were as dear to her as her own little Louise.

When we were growing up, our tutors stressed letter writing so we often wrote to our mama, papa and sisters in English and in French. I remember wishing Louise a happy birthday every year in little notes. I would send her letters full of love and would often teach her the lessons I learned from my teachers and my books, telling her of the mysteries of the universe long before she could understand them.

And I was always looking out for her, too. Our mama did not approve of candy for children. We were only allowed to have it once a year at Christmastime and little ones couldn't have it at all. I remember, when Louise had learned her alphabet, she was so proud of herself. That day I carefully penned one of my letters, begging mama to give her some bonbons. I wrote, "...Mama, she is just a little girl, so intelligent and sweet, you really cannot refuse her some sweets."

We were in the toy strewn playroom. Mama was embroidering a tablecloth while she watched little Louise play happily with her blocks.

"Well, my little Kate," mama replied with a smile as she lay down my note, "Bless your little heart, you are right. Sometimes I forget what it is like to be a little girl. Of course, Louise will have her treat."

Louise, who was building a house on the floor near mama's knee, knocked it down as she jumped up like a little frog to hug me. Laughing, she ran back to mama and gave her a kiss. Mama smiled at her little angel. She left the room and returned with a little box.

"Here, Louise, a sweet for a sweet little girl!" she said.

As I told you, we little girls had everything any child could wish for. One of our favorites was our playhouse. It was complete with carpets, child size furniture, and even a full kitchen, where we would pretend to bake and cook. Elizabeth, Louise, and I spent hours there pretending to be grown-ups and playing house. Of course, Louise was always the baby!

Sometimes she would tire of this and beg, "Katie, Lizzie, please let me be the mama, just once!"

Then we would pin her golden curls atop her head, dress her in the prettiest gown we could find, put her tiny feet into mama's old black high button shoes, and pretend to be her children.

*Katharine at age 7*

# Chapter 3

# Early Days

That reminds me of one of the first things I remember as a little girl. We often took trips to the Jersey shore where we would stay in a rambling gray house behind grassy dunes. There the squawking of sea gulls would be the first sound we heard each morning. One sunny day our whole family went to the beach. I liked to roll on the sand and collect seashells, but was petrified of the ocean. With my little pail, I would try to get some water, but I ran back each time that a wave would near the shore. Papa, mama, and Lizzie had waded into the water, laughing as they splashed and dipped under the waves. As I quietly observed them, tiptoeing cautiously toward the ocean and hurriedly running back to the sand as soon as a drop of water would touch my toe, my papa called me to follow him.

"Come here, Katie, take my hand."

"No, Papa. No!" I cried.

When he saw how afraid I was, he put me on his shoulders and walked out into the ocean. There I was piggyback with my little arms hugged tightly around his neck. The sea spray splashed into my face. Papa ducked and I was under the water. A big wave crashed over us. I was scared to death! I started coughing out water and clinging as tightly as I could, but somehow feeling safe in my father's arms. Strangely, when he brought me back to shore, my fear was gone and I was ready to go out again. I was proud of myself. I was a big girl like my sister! Many times in my life since then, I remember my new found courage. At that moment, little as I was, I felt my Heavenly Father's Arms were around me just as had been dear Papa's.

Under the guidance of my parents I was always very conscious of the love of God, our Father, and Jesus, His Son. Through my young years I watched as my parents and Lizzie walked to the altar at Mass. I longed to be able to receive Jesus in my heart like the rest of the family. Each year as I grew a little older, I yearned more and more to make my First Holy Communion, but I had to wait. In those days the Blessed Sacrament could not be received often and children were not considered ready till they were about twelve. The sisters at the convent nearby were my teachers. I paid attention to their every word and I studied very hard. I crossed the days off on my calendar with a bright red pencil. Little did anyone know how my heart ached for Jesus.

Finally, the special morning came. I was dressed in a beautiful white lace dress and white veil.

"Oh, Katie, how pretty you are," said Louise. "You look like an angel!"

We took a carriage to the nearby Convent of the Religious of the Sacred Heart. The horses trotted quickly along for they were as impatient as I was. Mama in a new blue dress and Papa in his best striped suit sat beside me proudly holding my hands. The convent was soon before our eyes. When we entered the doors, the sisters were waiting. I left my parents and joined a group of other children all dressed in their finest clothes — the girls in white dresses like me and the boys in white suits. We were marched up front where we sat quietly in a pew near the flower filled altar.

Bishop Wood and altar boys came out on the altar. We waited. The sermon reminded us to love Jesus. We waited. The collection plate was passed. We waited. Finally the priest lifted the Sacred Host and the bells chimed. At last! Folding my hands, touching finger to finger as perfectly as I could, I followed the line of boys and girls up the aisle to the communion rail. The organ played softly, the choir sang of Jesus, and I bowed my head in joyful prayer. And then, to add to my joy, the bishop confirmed us immediately after the end of Mass!

Afterwards we went back to the house where there was a great breakfast for all the family. Grandparents, uncles, aunts, and cousins sat at the long table in the dining room. It was very festive. Flowers were everywhere, candelabra burned on both ends of the table, and the servants placed more and more delicious food before us. When we children were finished, we went into the drawing room to play games. We spent the whole day together laughing and having fun.

Late afternoon everyone went home. I had been waiting all day for this. I ran upstairs to the oratory where I was alone at last. I lifted my long white skirt and knelt before the crucifix and the statue of Mary for a long time in silence. My heart was filled with joy but I could hardly say a word.

"Dear Jesus, thank you for coming to me,"

I prayed. As many tears ran down my cheeks, I made a promise, "I will always love You and stay close to You no matter what."

Even though we had the oratory in our home where the bishop or priests would sometimes come to say Mass, I loved to go to the nearby church where I would attend ten o'clock Mass with my parents.

My papa was so tall, so strong, so kind, so handsome — and so devoted to God. I remember every day when he would return from work, we would run into his arms and smother him with kisses, then he would go to his room for a half hour to speak with God. Afterward, he would often sit at his organ and play his favorite classical pieces while outside the door would be three little girls silently listening and patiently waiting. Sometimes he would call us in and we would sing little songs with him.

Even though I was devoted to Jesus, and tried not to be vain, I am afraid I did love all the beautiful things in my life. Our mother would have our clothes handmade and would take us with her as our dresses were being designed by the sisters in a nearby convent. These were made very simply without any frills. Elizabeth and Louise did not seem to mind, but I surely did. As we were leaving I would often run back to the room.

"Please, Sister, don't forget to put lots of lace and ruffles on my dress just like mama's," I begged.

# Chapter 4

# Grandparents

I told you I had three sets of grandparents. There were Grandmother Drexel, Grandfather and Grandmother Bouvier, and Grandmother Langstroth. We were very close to all of them and would get together with our many cousins at their homes. Grandmother Langstroth even had a room she called the Children's Playground, filled with every imaginable toy for us. All the girls especially enjoyed the dolls that came complete with trunks and wardrobes of clothes and always wanted to play with them.

Usually the cousins would share, but that was not always the case. When we were playing house, everyone wanted a lot of children. One day my cousin Bessie took six dolls and Lizzie took seventeen. That was it! I was usually a happy sharing little girl and tried to emulate my parents who always were generous and kind. I didn't complain as long as I had at least one doll, but this was too much! There was no doll left for me. I ran down the stairs, crying quietly.

"Grandma, Grandma!" I sobbed as I entered the parlor.

Quickly Grandmother removed her glasses, dropped her book, and gathered me in her arms.

"Katie darling, what is it?" she asked.

Through my sobs I answered her and begged, "Grandma, can't I have just one teeny-weeny doll for myself?" Of course, Grandma flew right up those stairs.

"Bessie, Lizzie, how can you be so selfish? I am ashamed of you. Now, both of you let Katie have some babies right away!"

After that I was never left out again.

But, I am sorry to say, my dear Grandmother Langstroth, who was not a Catholic, had her problems with us. One evening we went to her house for dinner. Though the food was always delicious, we didn't eat much as there was something on our minds.

"Girls, are you sick?" Grandma asked as she noticed our full plates.

We looked at each other and Lizzie said sadly, "Oh Grandma, I am so sorry for you because you can never go to Heaven!" Quietly putting down her fork, Grandma stared at her.

"And why can't Grandmother go to Heaven?" she asked.

"You are a Protestant and Protestants never go to Heaven," Lizzie and I replied together.

You can imagine how stunned she was by this information which we had picked up from one of the servants. She said no more, but when my papa came to pick us up, she met him with a stern face. Her usual welcoming smile was not there to greet him.

"Mother, what's the matter?" he asked.

"Frank," she responded, "how are you raising my granddaughters?"

Papa, who was so very holy and good, was taken aback by her angry demeanor. You can imagine his horror when she told him what had happened. He turned to his two daughters who were waiting near the door shaking.

"Girls, where did you hear this nonsense?"

"But Joanna told us, Papa," I replied mentioning a servant girl at home.

"Well, this is not true," he said as he gave us a little lecture on our religious beliefs. "We'll straighten this out when we get home. Now go apologize to grandma."

"Oh, Grandma, I am so sorry. I love you. Please forgive me," I pleaded.

I hugged her tightly and kissed her, happy to be in her good graces once more.

Poor Grandmother Langstroth, she really put up with a lot from her little granddaughters. It's a wonder she ever invited us to dinner. On another occasion, we learned a Protestant minister would be saying the grace before meals. Lizzie and I didn't know what to do, so after a little consultation in the living room, we decided to hold up our rosary beads to show that we were Catholics!

We loved not only Grandmother Langstroth, but all our grandparents and enjoyed spending time with them. After ten o'clock Mass, papa would take us for a visit with Grandmother and Grandfather Bouvier where we played with our cousins while the grown-ups talked and on Sunday afternoons we would visit Grandma Drexel. As these were all Catholics, I don't remember any such hurtful moments with them.

# Chapter 5

# School Days

I know you are thinking now how different my world was from yours, but I want to tell you all about me so you will understand why the two priests chose to call on us and how this surprise visit changed my life.

One late spring day when we were young, with summer just around the corner, we noticed there was a lot of activity around our house. Mother was consulting with a carpenter upstairs and father was in his den studying some blue papers.

"It looks like mama and papa are fixing up the corner bedroom," I told Lizzie.

"I guess we are having important visitors," she answered. "I wonder who it is."

We went out with our nurse for a walk down Walnut Street to Rittenhouse Square and promptly forgot about it. Our chattering was all about our coming trip to the country.

Summer came and went. When we returned home in the fall, mother called us into the parlor.

"Come upstairs," she said, "You must close your eyes. I have a surprise for you."

We ran up the steps not knowing what to expect. When we opened our eyes we saw the bedroom upstairs had been remodeled, but not for sleeping. We stopped at the doorway to see a bright and cheery classroom. There was a wall of bookshelves filled from end to end. There were three desks, even a tiny one for Louise. On each there were pencils, papers, pens, and an inkwell. On the walls were maps of the United States and the world and framed art prints. Over by the window hung a large basket of greens and the windowsills were covered with plants. There was even a large table filled with many brushes, tubes of paint, and pads of paper over in the corner.

"Now, our little girls are going to start school," said papa with a big smile and a touch to his moustache. "How do you like that!"

We clapped our hands. This was a new adventure.

"But papa, who will be the teacher?" I asked him.

"Don't worry about that," he replied. "You will have the best education anywhere."

We learned that papa and mama had already arranged to have the finest tutors for everything — reading, writing, arithmetic, and Latin, French, literature, and music! Our most important teacher was Miss Cassidy, who kept us busy writing essays and letters to our parents, friends, and sisters — even though we lived in the same house! And she made us do this in both English and French!

We loved Miss Cassidy and I know it was through her hard work that we all learned to express ourselves so well in writing. It wasn't easy for a little girl to write a letter in another language, but thanks to her hard work, we were able to do it. And we wrote long letters to Miss Cassidy wherever we went long after we were grown.

When it came to religion, mama and papa taught us that God came first. They did this as much by actions as by words. My parents shared their wealth and taught us to do the same. Though we sometimes studied with the sisters at the convent nearby, our mother kept a close eye on our religious education. We read and discussed the lives of many saints. Our favorite was St. Francis of Assisi, papa's patron saint. We were very impressed by this rich young man who gave up all his wealth to follow Jesus. We wondered how he could do it and thought of how great was his love for God.

Summers were always special. Not only did we flee to our country home, but then came the fun times of our education. Our father felt we should see America first, so we traveled together throughout the United States to all the important historical and geographical points of interest. I remember especially our trips to the White Mountains, to Maine, California, Colorado, the Great Lakes, and to New Orleans. There was so much to see and we girls had a wonderful time. Though we never got tired, or bored, sometimes the hikes were a bit much for our parents! I remember once when papa refused to go a step further while mama urged him on. They had a little "battle of words" about it and Lizzie, alarmed, knelt down to say some prayers in the middle of the woods, using a rock for her kneeling bench. All's well that ends well, for I think, thanks to Elizabeth's intercession with the Lord, we continued merrily on our way.

As we got older we went overseas to visit the cultural and religious places in Europe. One year we sailed across the sea on a huge ocean liner and never came home till the following May. It was great fun and a perfect way to learn! We toured England, France, Switzerland, Austria, and Italy. We visited cathedrals, monasteries, museums, and art galleries, and even a few beaches where we relaxed in the sun and took a break from our travels.

# Chapter 6

# New Beginnings

When I was almost twelve papa bought a new home for us in the country in a small town called Torresdale. This was nothing like the old one which had been small and cozy. This one was on ninety acres and included cottages for servants, a stable, a barn, and a carriage house. The old farm house was remodeled for us. There was a statue of St. Michael carved in stone above the front door, and even a stained glass window of this saint on the first floor landing! It was like this archangel was watching over us wherever we went!

If you knew my father, you would like him. He was so warm and loving. He cared so much for us and wanted everything to be perfect for his little daughters. Before we moved in the gardeners planted sloping lawns, trees, and flower beds till all our surroundings were totally beautiful. Lizzie, Louise and I called our new home, "the Nest."

Our mother was just as kind and generous. You would like her, too. Everybody did. When we were staying in Philadelphia, the doors of our home were thrown open three afternoons a week to the poor. Clothing, medicine, and rent money were given readily to those in need. While other wealthy women were playing bridge or shopping, she sat with the poor and offered them a warm heart and a helping hand.

"Madam, you are so kind. Thank you, thank you," we heard so many times.

Soon we were allowed to help out. Somehow it made us feel close to God, almost like St. Francis.

As I told you we were very rich. Although our grandfather was a famous artist and an international banker, papa had to start out working at the counter in the bank and his pay was small. He even played the organ in a church to earn extra money. Gradually his father felt faith in him and gave him more responsibility. After his father died, papa inherited a great deal of money. He was thankful for every penny that had been given to him.

Papa told us, "Girls, we have been very blessed. God has entrusted us with this wealth as a means of helping others. We must always share what we have and give from the heart."

"Papa, we always will. We want to be like you and mama," I replied, never realizing then what that promise would mean.

It was time to put into practice the lessons we had learned from both our parents. It was a perfect June day and we had just settled in our new home. Mama was sitting on the front porch reading while we sat on the top step playing a game of jacks. Our pet dog lay on the grass with his tail wagging, impatiently waiting for us to walk with him.

"Lizzie, Katie," mama interrupted us, "I have been thinking. How would you like to start a Sunday School for the children whose fathers work on our place?"

"Oh, Mama, what a great idea," we exclaimed together. "We love little children and it will be fun."

Mama got us some books, small Bibles, and lots of paper and pencils for drawing the biblical stories. Lizzie taught the older children and I, the younger ones. After the lessons, we gathered the children around the piano in the parlor and sang hymns. At first, there weren't many children, but after a few years there were fifty or more boys and girls who came every Sunday. I think we became good little teachers.

Each year we closed for the winter to go back to the city, but we always had a special party where we celebrated Jesus' birth with candy, cakes, and special gifts for each child. We gathered around the candlelit tree and the little manger the children had made and sang Christmas carols while papa played the piano.

Another blessing for our family, and especially me, during that time was that the pastor of the nearby St. Dominic's Church, Father O'Connor, became good friends with us. He noticed my spiritual leanings and encouraged me to keep a diary. I thought this was a neat idea as it would help me to be better behaved. Like you, I am sure, I tried very hard to be good, but knew I had faults to deal with. My worst fault, I believed, was pride and vanity. As I told you I loved pretty things and was very conscious of how I looked, especially as a teenager. I also noticed there were times I said my prayers without really thinking. Those were just some of the things I had to work on. I even made myself a little checklist to see how I was doing.

Sometimes I did not do very well. I would make resolutions for Lent and fail miserably in keeping them. Still, I know I did try and try my hardest, and kept on trying even after I failed. I felt God loved me and would understand that this young girl was doing her best.

# Chapter 7

# Many Changes

On July 2, 1878 when I was eighteen, I finished my formal education. As with all teenagers at that point in their lives, there was a mixture of joy and sadness in my heart. It is something you look forward to and all the sudden it is there — a perpetual vacation from books and study, you think. But, on the other hand, before that, there was a definite future to look for — graduation! Suddenly everything is new and uncertain. Still, I was happy.

An exciting time for me was the following January when I made my debut. This was the day when a wealthy girl who had been sheltered for her whole life, formally was presented to society. It is a stepping stone to the future — it means she is now part of the adult world. My parents threw a grand party, my mother had the seamstress make me the most beautiful gown, and all our friends and relatives came. An orchestra filled the room with music. There was dancing and plenty of food of every variety, and I was the center of attention. Though I still had problems with my pride and vanity, my heart told me something was missing here.

One thing it did mean was all that summer both at the shore and at home, there were many parties and many young men suddenly appearing in my life.

*Emma Bouvier Drexel*

Lizzie and I did enjoy that! There were beach picnics and gatherings every night. Of course, this was a cause of concern to our papa. While we were away, he wrote often and warned us not to "get into deep water either with the beaus or the surf." And we didn't!

Something was wrong with mama. Even though she tried to hide it, we could see it.

"Mama, are you okay?" I asked her in the fall. But she smiled and reassured me.

"Yes, my darling, don't worry about me. I am just a little tired lately. I have been running too much. That's all," she replied.

But she was not okay. We later learned she had gone to our home in Philadelphia to have the doctor perform an operation.

"I don't want to worry the family," mama had told him. "I will hire a nurse and since it is only minor surgery, my bedroom will do just fine. Frank and the girls won't need to know. They would just worry needlessly. I'll give them an excuse for going to Philadelphia."

The doctor reluctantly agreed. Now this could never happen today. But it was a different time then. Operations were rare and instruments and operating rooms were not sterile. Doctors came to the home with their little black bags and made house calls if you were sick. Father found out too late to change anything. He went to our Philadelphia home and found mama in her bed very weak and in great pain.

"Emma, Emma, oh, why did you let anyone do this?" he cried as he held his sick wife in his arms.

The cause of her pain was cancer!

For three years she suffered. At times the pain was almost unbearable, but through it all she never complained. I was her special nurse and did everything for her. I wanted to be near her every minute. I watched her fail from week to week, and from day to day until at the end she was almost fading away before my eyes. As I watched her in the pale candlelight dressed in a white nightgown, it seemed she was already an angel from heaven. I sat with her at night, praying with her, and telling her how much I loved her. Yet, my mother's thoughts were only for us. When papa came to sit with her, she held his hand tightly and whispered her love for him.

"Oh, Frank, my dearest one, how I pray that when your time comes, you will be spared all this. I have offered the pain I suffer for you," she said as papa tearfully held her in his arms and tried to comfort her, his loving Emma.

I never dreamed our little family circle would be broken. I could not bear to think of being separated from my parents and sisters. Now that horrible moment had come. On February 1st, my mama closed her eyes and died. I sat beside her for a long time and talked to her. I hoped she heard my words of love. I held her hand till they took me away and placed tall candles at her bedside.

"Oh, Mama, how can we bear it without you?" I cried.

Papa spent the night in her room.

She was gone from us! Hundreds of people came to her funeral — rich and poor alike. Her goodness had touched them all and sorrow filled their hearts. But to us, her family, it was the worst time you could imagine. We girls couldn't stop weeping and after the funeral, papa retired to his room and played the organ for hours and hours as if he wanted to pour out in music his grief that was almost too heavy to bear. And once again, we waited outside the door.

We were all so sad and couldn't seem to get over our grief. That fall Papa decided to take us on a tour of Europe to try to get our minds off our sorrow. It did help and we were away until springtime. Mama was with God, but we felt she was with us and we still thought of her all the time.

One evening, shortly after our return, papa came home from work. The routine was no different than any other night. He went to his room to pray, he played the organ, and we then sat down to dinner. We talked about everyday things, how we had spent our day, plans for the future, things like that. After we had eaten our dessert, the servants cleared away the dishes.

"We'll have coffee in the library," Papa informed them as he rose from the table.

We followed him. The library was dark, lit only by the candles on the walnut paneled walls. It was a cozy room where we had spent long hours reading and talking together. Surrounded by our treasured books and love, we were comfortable. Papa slowly took a cigar from the humidor on the desk and lit it. Then he made an announcement.

"Girls," he said, "I have something to tell you. I have accomplished something today that I am sure will please you."

We waited expectantly as he seemed so happy. He was always full of exciting plans. What was it this time?

"Papa, tell us what you have done," exclaimed Lizzie as Louise and I leaned toward him.

"I have made my will," he replied smiling at us.

"Oh, Papa, what does that mean?" we cried out together. "Papa, are you sick?"

"No, my darlings," he answered. "I just want to protect you from fortune hunters when I die."

When he died, oh, no, our papa couldn't die and leave us, too! He went on to explain his wishes, but we could hardly pay attention. There was a foreboding in our hearts.

A year later papa did die! It happened so fast — first he had a cold, then pleurisy, then suddenly he was gone! I was with him most of the time that week, fixing his pillows, taking his temperature, dosing him with cough medicine — all those little things that soothe the sick, make them comfortable, and show your love.

One late afternoon he seemed to feel better. As he sat in his favorite spot by the window reading the newspaper, I went to the next room to get him a glass of cool water. I heard a sound. I ran in and found him slumped in his chair. I screamed and screamed for help. Lizzie, Louise, and the servants came running. There was no such thing as a telephone. We sent a servant for the doctor. I grabbed my coat, and ran as fast as I could to St. Patrick's Rectory where I pounded on the door and begged loudly, "Come quick, my father is dying!" As the priest and I came out the door, one of the servants was there with a carriage waiting for us. We rushed home, but it was all in vain. Papa was dead!

"Oh, papa," I cried and cried, "don't leave us. We need you."

I hardly remember the funeral. I know thousands of people came, but it was all a blur. We saw the bronze casket surrounded by flowers, held many hands, kissed many cheeks, but still could not believe it. Only our faith in God got us through those days.

But this is where my story began. Have you ever had a sudden change in your life? Maybe your dad was transferred in his job and you had to move far away to another state or country where everything was different, or maybe someone close to you died. It is like you have to open a door, but you don't know what is on the other side and you are not sure you will like what you find. To me, that door opened in my life when I walked into the drawing room on a winter evening. I was led to a strange land and as I journeyed forward, my eyes were opened to what God had planned for me.

Remember the two priests from the Indian Missions? That night the butler had ushered them into the drawing room. He lit the fire and then came upstairs for us. As they told me their story, I learned they were looking for financial aid to further Catholic education of the Indians out West, a place I knew little about. I sat on the couch, completely engrossed, for hours as Father showed me pictures of the Indians and their living conditions. He took out papers and explained how various programs by the United States had failed and how the Indians were suffering in poverty and lack of education. And nobody cared!

"The Government's plan to aid the Indians is not succeeding. We have heard of your kindness and generosity," they told me. "Will you help us?" they begged.

I listened to every word. Our papa had taught us to share our wealth, but we had never heard of anything so sad! After a time, I had the butler serve them coffee while I went upstairs to get my sisters. They were filled with compassion, too. And this was the beginning of a long journey which led to a surprise ending for me.

# Chapter 8

# A Journey to the Future

I was greatly moved by the plight of the Indians and told Father I would gladly lend my support which I did, sending many checks to him as he kept me up-to-date on how the money was used. But papa's death had taken a lot out of me. I became very sick and for a year was weak and tired. Finally, my doctor advised a trip to Europe where I would spend five weeks in the healing waters of a spa. We decided to go. It was just what I needed. I rested, took mud baths, and drank the healing waters of the spring.

Soon I was strong enough to consider our mission. Lizzie, Louise, and I had decided to study school methods and building construction that could be used for our Indian schools. We stayed in the finest hotels and enjoyed every comfort that money could buy, but our main objective was the schools which over the past year had become very important to us. We had already built a boarding school. Though it was completed, the big problem was getting people to run it and teachers to educate the little boys and girls. We needed missionaries and thought we would find help overseas. We visited several European monasteries begging them to send priests and sisters, but we were out of luck. None were interested. None would come.

*Katharine Drexel*

Finally, we arrived in Rome. We went to the Vatican where we would attend Mass and have a private audience with Pope Leo XIII. For days I had looked forward to this meeting. He was the head of the whole Catholic Church. I knew he would be able to help us. He would find us missionaries!

We wore black veils and long sleeved dresses. As we entered the Vatican's imposing structure, we were met by the Holy Father's secretary who told us the Pope was expecting us. Down long, many windowed hallways, we followed the priest as he told us the proper procedure for meeting with the pope. We entered a huge room. The Holy Father rose to greet us. Tears were in my eyes as I knelt at his feet and kissed his ring. I knew our time with him would be short, so I came right out with my story. I told him about the Indians in America. Surely, this would move his heart!

"Your Holiness, it is all so sad. I know you will find an answer. Won't you send missionaries?" I begged.

He looked at me gravely. I knew he was going to make a suggestion that would bring Christianity and aid to the Indians, and I waited hopefully for his words.

His answer burned my soul. "Why not, my child, you yourself become a missionary?"

"Because, Holy Father, sisters can be had for the missions, but no priests," I replied.

What happened after that, I am not sure. All I know is when he said this, I became sick all over, so sick I could not get out of the Vatican quickly enough. Once outside, I sobbed and sobbed so much my sisters didn't know what to do with me! They hailed a carriage and hurried me back to the hotel where I went to my room and fell sound asleep.

I was really frightened. When I agreed to help the Indians, I never expected anything like this. Oh, I loved God and I had had serious thoughts of serving him in some way, but not this! I was not cut out to be a missionary! I know many young girls like the Little Flower felt the call when they were very young. I have read Therese Martin even went to Pope Leo XIII around the same time as I did and, though she was only fourteen, begged him to allow her to enter the Carmelites Order of nuns. Throughout my life, I had read of many other saints who had received the call from God at even eleven or twelve, but I was 28!

By the time we returned home, more and more appeals were coming from the desperate Indian missions, and we set out to visit them ourselves. This time there were no grand hotels. We were really roughing it. We took a train to Nebraska. From there on Lizzie and Louise rode horseback over rocky trails while I bumped along in a wagon with our priest escorts. There were no motels or hotels so we stayed at the various missions on the reservations. We talked to Indians. We held their ragged children in our arms. And we thought of our own upbringing — beautiful clothes, perfect home, and plenty of food to eat.

"Oh, Father," I told our priest friend. "My heart aches for these people. I never dreamed it was this bad. We will do everything we can to help."

We poured more and more money into the missions and the boarding schools, but still the question remained, who would teach in them? Was I really being called by God? Was Pope Leo XIII right? I was far from sure.

When we arrived home, I couldn't think of anything else. I made lists for and against my entering religious life. Mainly, I couldn't be separated from my family; I didn't think I could bear community life, or taking orders from Superiors; I had never been without luxuries, how could I follow poverty? I was tormented by uncertainty. Louise had married and now it was just Lizzie and me. I knew that soon she would wed and I would be alone. It wasn't that there were a lack of men and dates in my life. In fact, one young man was seriously pursuing me with flowers and candy and protestations of love, but I was not interested.

Father O'Connor, who was my dear friend, was now a bishop. I decided to confide in him whom I trusted to know me well. We wrote long letters back and forth. He discouraged me saying he felt I could better do God's work by sharing my wealth and remaining out in the world.

"By no means should you enter the convent!" he stated firmly.

I would tell him of my inward yearnings. Still, he was adamant.

"No, Katie, that life is not for you," he insisted.

The more convinced I became, the more he said no. This went on for years. I had been close to him since childhood and I felt I should heed his advice. I continued to pray. Then, finally out of the blue, I received the word I had been waiting for.

"Katie, I think you do have a vocation," he wrote. "And I think you should start a new order of sisters devoted to the Indians."

Oh, no! This last thought scared me. My wish was the quiet life of a contemplative nun. Now, what was I to do about this?

*Father Stephan, Marty and Mother Katharine (second from left) at Mission on western visit.*

# Chapter 9

# Finding the Way

By this time Lizzie and Louise were well aware of my love for the Indian missions and my longing to become a sister — and they believed God was calling me. The rest of the family did not suspect. All my cousins and aunts and uncles didn't have a clue as far as I knew.

One afternoon, I went to visit my cousin, Molly. It was a beautiful spring-like day in early March. Clouds drifted overhead. We were sitting on the glider in the sun porch overlooking the gardens as the servants served us tea and cookies. She was full of her plans for the summer at the shore that she hoped we would share. I decided it was time to break the news to her.

"Molly, guess what I am going to do?" I asked.

Smiling happily and grabbing my hands, she answered, "Oh, Katie, you're getting married. I am so excited. Who is it?"

"No, Moll," I replied. "I am going into the convent!"

She turned white. "Oh, Katie, I can't believe it! Are you serious?"

We hadn't talked since Christmastime, so I told her all about my inward yearnings, my long days of indecision, my final realization that this was right for me. She had known me all my life — she understood.

"Oh, Katie, I am so happy for you," she finally said as she leaned over and kissed my cheek.

My Uncle Anthony walked in just then. He carefully placed his briefcase on the floor next to a big pot of greens and gave me a strange look. I knew he had overheard part of our conversation. He patted Molly's shoulder then turned to me.

"What's this all about? What are you girls up to?" he asked.

I told him my plans.

"Katie, I guess I should have seen this coming. You have always been close to God, but being close to God is one thing, going into the convent is another."

Pounding his fist on the back of a chair, he added, "Katie, your papa is not here to advise you, but I am. I think this is the biggest mistake of your life! Don't rush into this!"

When he learned that this was not a rash decision, but one I had been pondering over for years, he wiped a few tears from his eyes and put his arms around me.

"All right, Kitten, whatever you do, I'll be here for you. I am your uncle. You know you can call on me for anything."

Soon after that, the whole family knew what Katie had decided to do with her life.

Now I had to move on. There was much discussion back and forth with Bishop O'Connor who felt it best that I join an order of nuns to be trained and experience convent life. He mentioned several choices, but I decided I would like to train with the Sisters of Mercy. All the arrangements were made and on May 7, 1889, Katie, the wealthy Drexel girl, became a postulant, secluded from everything she had ever known in a convent in Pittsburgh, Pennsylvania!

I adapted very nicely to nunnery ways and six months later came the big day of my reception. Lizzie and Louise bought me the most beautiful white gown trimmed with orange blossoms — and lots of lace and ruffles. I wore diamond rings and a diamond necklace and eight little girls in white satin dresses and white veils followed me up the aisle. No wedding could have been more lovely. That day I became the bride of Christ! I made my vows, which meant I gave up my beautiful clothes and jewels and all the luxuries of my life forever. Now I would live in poverty, chastity, and obedience, and wear the dark somber dress of a nun. Like the St. Francis of Assisi that I learned of long ago, I gave up everything for Jesus — and at long last I understood how Francis was able to do it.

Although the situation of the Indians still caused me pain, I troubled over the idea of starting a new order to serve them and didn't feel that I was up to it. It just didn't seem right for me.

"Katie, there is no doubt in my mind. This is what God wants you to do," decided Bishop O'Connor. "You have both love for the Indians and a good head for business. You were born for this! You will have no problems getting it all together and, you may be sure, I will help you, too, in whatever way I am able."

So with faith in God and courage in my heart, I trusted the priest who had been my advisor for so long. I accepted this challenge as my mission in life. On February 12, 1891, I vowed myself to God and the

Sisters of the Blessed Sacrament was born. Thirteen other novices joined me and together we would make this journey, knowing the hand of God would guide us through the unknown territory ahead.

As I donned the black veil of sisterhood that morning, I looked back over my life. I knew that God had led me to this moment from the time I was a little child saying the rosary in the chapel, praising the Lord in the country, and teaching Sunday School in the parlor. Nursing my dying parents and visiting the Holy Father had opened my eyes to my place in the world. I was ready to give my life to God and would follow whatever path He lay before me.

I looked from the candle-lit altar in front of the church to my closest relatives, filling the oak pews, sharing this day with me. Joy filled my heart. Oh, yes, I knew I had come a long way — even I was surprised at where I had ended up — with still a very long way to go. Now, I knew all about the "Indian Missions." The fairy tale was coming to an end. And I knew I would be happy ever after.

DARKNESS lay on the bayou—

DARKNESS lay on the fields—

DARKNESS lay in the souls of black folk.

DARKNESS in cotton fields.

"NO HOPE" moaned the wind o'er the meadow.

"NO HOPE" sobbed the winds 'round the lea.

"NO HOPE" wept the trees in the forest.

"NO HOPE" said the Christ, "Save in Me."

A woman walked on the bayou.

A woman walked in the fields.

A woman prayed for the souls of the black folk.

A woman wept for the minds of black folk.

A woman — in cotton fields.

"Sweet Lord, here is land for a harvest,

Dear God, here are souls for Thee."

"Sweet Savior," she whispered, "please answer

If the work of these fields be for me."

The answer was given, "Go child."

She went — through cloistered portals.

She went — as a nun — for the souls of black folk.

She went — as a nun — for the minds of black folk.

She went to bring God to mortals.

"Here's hope," sang the wind o'er the meadow.

"Here's hope," hummed the wind 'round the lea.

"Here's hope," laughed the tree in the forest.

"Here's hope," said Christ. "Come to Me."

Hazel Thomas,
St. Francis de Sales High School,
Rock Castle, Virginia

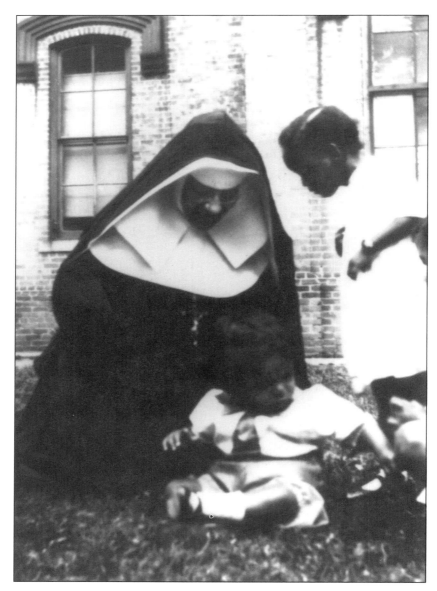

*Mother Katharine with child.*

# Afterword

On February 12, 1891, Katharine Drexel pronounced her vows as the first Sister of the Blessed Sacrament. She would now be called Mother Katharine Mary. With thirteen companions, she returned to St. Michael's.

In 1892 they moved to St. Elizabeth's Convent in Cornwells Heights, Pennsylvania. The burden of administration and guidance rested on her for forty-four years.

Missionary work began with the opening of a boarding school for Black children, and then one among the Pueblo Indians of New Mexico. Mother Katharine established many ministries starting in 1891. In 1902, St. Michael's School, on the Navajo Indian reservation, was opened. She led a life devoted to uplifting the minds and spirits of Native and African American women, men, and children.

Founding and staffing these schools for both Native and African Americans throughout the country became a priority for Mother Katharine and her congregation. During her lifetime, she opened, staffed, and directly supported nearly sixty schools and missions. As the years passed, boarding and day schools were opened in the East, the Midwest, and in the rural and urban areas of the South and Southwest. In 1917, a school to prepare teachers was established in New Orleans, which received a charter in 1925 as Xavier University of New Orleans, the only predominantly Black Catholic institution of higher learning in the United States.

In 1935, Mother Katharine suffered a severe heart attack, and for the next twenty years lived in prayerful retirement. Her interest and love for the missions deepened, until her death on March 3, 1955. She is interred in the crypt of the Motherhouse Chapel, the Mother Katharine Drexel Shrine. Mother Katharine's Sisters of the Blessed Sacrament have faithfully continued her work for social justice since her death.

www.katharinedrexel.org

For a full account of Mother Katharine Drexel's missionary days we suggest:

**Katharine Drexel: A Biography**
by Sister Consuela Marie Duffy, S.B.S.
Sisters of the Blessed Sacrament
Bensalem, PA 19020

## The Fortune

During her lifetime Katharine Drexel invested an estimated $20 million in service to the African and Native American communities. According to the terms of her father's will, all monies were distributed to other charities at her death.

According to this will, which went into effect upon his death in 1885, 90% of Francis A. Drexel's estate was placed in Trust for his three daughters. Ten percent (10%) was distributed to various charities. Income was to be distributed to the daughters during their lifetime. This trust was to be terminated at the death of the last surviving daughter and the principal to be distributed to heirs. When Katharine died in 1955, there were no heirs and the principal was distributed to the original charities who had received 10% at the death of Mr. Drexel.

The $14 million trust estate was distributed to 28 Catholic charitable, educational, and religious institutions, and one Lutheran Hospital.

The Sisters of the Blessed Sacrament were not founded until after Mr. Drexel's death and, therefore, they did not share in this distribution. The income they had been receiving ceased upon Mother Katharine's death. Some of the charities did make contributions to the Sisters of the Blessed Sacrament at the request of Archbishop O'Hara.

www.katharinedrexel.org

*Jack, Jeanette and Amy Wall*
*December, 1993*

## The Miracle

Amanda (Amy) Wall of Bucks County, Pennsylvania was born with nerve deafness in both ears in 1992. Her incurable deafness was confirmed by medical tests completed in September 1993. Her parents accepted this and prayed to Blessed Katharine Drexel to be a good family and to learn how to communicate with Amy. They learned about a deaf school and sign language. Her father was even seeking a new job in Washington, D.C. so they could move close to Gallaudet University where they planned to send Amy to school.

In the last week of February 1994, Jack, who was eight, suggested to his mother that they all pray to Blessed Katharine Drexel to intercede for Amy's cure. Five year old Jeanette's prayer was that if Amy could not hear, that she become deaf, so that they could be true sisters, the same. Constance Wall, who knew that prayer to Mother Katharine had resulted in the restoration of hearing to Robert Gutherman's right ear, agreed to pray with her children. She saw this as a time of family togetherness and hope, although she did not expect a miracle.

But Jack and Jeanette did call for a miracle and it was their pure faith, their knowing without doubt that through God all is possible that led to the family's prayer. Within a week of beginning to pray, Amy could hear! It was in March 1994 that a preschool teacher recognized a change in Amy's responses and told Mrs. Wall. The family was amazed and deeply grateful to God. When Amy began to speak, she spoke not in baby talk but in sentences. New hearing tests were administered and she was found to have normal hearing in both ears. Further tests confirmed this.

The Medical Board at the Vatican in Rome investigated and declared: "There is no natural cause for this cure attributed to Blessed Katharine Drexel." Pope John Paul II designated October 1, 2000 as Mother Katharine Drexel's canonization date.

She will be the first American born, Catholic born saint.

# Chronology

| | |
|---|---|
| 1858 | born Katharine Mary Drexel in Philadelphia on November 26. |
| 1858 | baptized Church of the Assumption on December 29. |
| 1858 | mother, Hannah Langstroth Drexel, died on December 30. |
| 1860 | father, Francis Anthony Drexel, married Emma Bouvier on April 10. |
| 1860 | bought a summer place in Nicetown. |
| 1863 | grandfather, Francis Martin Drexel, died on June 6. |
| 1863 | sister, Louise Drexel, was born on October 2. |
| 1870 | made First Holy Communion and Confirmation. |
| 1870 | new summer home in Torresdale purchased. |
| 1872 | Father James O'Connor became pastor of St. Dominic Church. |
| 1878 | finished education on July 2. |
| 1879 | made debut into society January 1. |
| 1883 | mother, Emma Drexel, died on January 29. |
| 1885 | father, Francis Drexel, died on February 15. |
| 1885 | first aware of Indian Missions in February. |
| 1887 | met with Pope Leo XIII on January 27. |
| 1888 | Father O'Connor agreed to Katharine's vocation on November 30. |

| 1889 | entered novitiate of Sisters of Mercy on May 7. |
| --- | --- |
| 1889 | reception into the religious life on November 7. |
| 1889 | sister, Louise Drexel, married Edward Morrell on January 17. |
| 1890 | sister, Elizabeth Drexel, married Walter George Smith on January 7. |
| 1890 | sister, Elizabeth Drexel Smith, died on September 26. |
| 1891 | professed vows. Sisters of the Blessed Sacrament born on February 12. |
| 1891-1955 | established missions throughout Midwest and South for Blacks and Indians. |
| 1935 | suffered heart attack. |
| 1945 | sister, Louise Drexel Morrell, died. |
| 1955 | Mother Katharine Drexel died on March 3. |
| 1987 | declared Venerable on January 26 by Pope John Paul. |
| 1988 | Beatified by Pope John Paul II on November 20. |
| 2000 | Canonized on October 1 by Pope John Paul II. |

# Glossary

| | |
|---|---|
| adamant | utterly unyielding in attitude or opinion. |
| advisor | one who gives advice. |
| beau | a girl's sweetheart. |
| bonbon | a small chocolate-covered candy. |
| butler | the chief male servant in a household. |
| candelabra | an ornamental branched candle holder for more than one candle. |
| chandelier | a decorative ornate light suspended from the ceiling. |
| chapel | a private place of prayer. |
| chastity | a state of being pure. |
| compassion | a feeling of deep sympathy. |
| condolence | expression of sympathy with a person who is suffering sorrow. |
| contemplative | a person devoted to thoughtful meditation and prayer. |
| cultural | pertaining to improvement of the mind. |
| cummerbund | a wide sash wore at the waist, especially with a tuxedo. |
| debut | a formal introduction into society. |
| desperate | reckless or dangerous because of despair. |

| | |
|---|---|
| drawing room | a private reception room in a private house. |
| embroidering | working ornamental designs upon cloth with thread and needle. |
| emulate | to imitate. |
| fascinate | to attract and hold intently. |
| financial | pertaining to money matters. |
| gracious | pleasantly kind. |
| geographical | pertaining to the natural features of a region. |
| harsh | ungentle or unpleasant in action. |
| humidor | a container suited to keeping cigars fresh. |
| kerosene | a widely used fuel. |
| mourning | the outer showing of sorrow. |
| monastery | a place of residence for people who have made religious vows. |
| nunnery | a convent for nuns or sisters. |
| ominous | threatening. |
| oratory | a place of prayer; a small chapel. |
| orphaned | to lose both parents. |
| petrified | to be numb with strong emotion such as fear. |
| pleurisy | a sickness of the lungs characterized by a dry cough and pain in the side. |
| portfolio | a flat portable case for carrying papers. |

| | |
|---|---|
| postulant | a candidate for admission to a religious order. |
| rectory | a house for a member of the clergy. |
| reveled | to take great pleasure in. |
| routine | a habitual or usual way of doing something. |
| slump | to fall heavily. |
| spa | a mineral spring. |
| sterile | free from germs. |
| tiara | a jeweled ornament worn by a woman like a crown on her head. |
| tutor | a teacher. |
| ushered | to show someone to their seat. |
| vows | a solemn promise. |
| whimpered | to cry with a low plaintive sound. |

# About the Author

CLAIRE JORDAN MOHAN, formerly of King of Prussia and Lansdale, now resides in Chalfont, Pennsylvania with her husband, Robert. Having retired from full-time teaching at Visitation B.V.M. School in Trooper, PA, she spends her time writing, traveling, and enjoying her grandchildren.

She has had many articles published in magazines and newspapers and has appeared on national radio and television shows, including Mother Angelica Live, the 700 Club, and CNBC.

On a recent trip to Rome for the Beatification of Blessed Frances Siedliska, Claire Mohan presented a special edition of her book *A Red Rose for Frania* to Pope John Paul II. Her recent book *The Young Life of Pope John Paul II* was also hand-delivered to Our Holy Father.

She is the mother of five children and grandmother of twelve. Claire is a graduate of Little Flower High School and is a 1984 summa cum laude graduate of Villanova University where she was valedictorian of her class. She attended Chestnut Hill College and West Chester University for graduate studies.

# *Other Books*

### *by Claire Jordan Mohan*

### Mother Teresa's Someday

School children delight in this beautifully illustrated story that tells the details of Mother Teresa's young life as a child in Yugoslavia. This account of her childhood is filled with joyful family experiences shared with her parents, brother, and sister.

### A Red Rose for Frania

This children's book offers young readers a thoughtful endearing story of Frances Siedliska's joys and struggles on her pathway to sainthood.

This story demonstrates courage and perseverance as it describes Frania's poor health and obstacles in committing to religious life.

### Kaze's True Home

This delightful story of the young life of Maria Kaupas will inspire each child as young Casimira follows her star to attain "the impossible dream." "Kaze" as she was called, was neither wealthy nor did she enjoy the opportunities of the young people of today, but she loved God and was able to share her love with others.

### The Young Life of Pope John Paul II

Young and old will enjoy this story which details the young life of Pope John Paul II while a boy in Poland. The way Karol Wojtyla handles the triumphs of his life will inspire children to emulate this courageous boy. They learn his life was just like theirs — a mixture of sadness and joy. They meet "a real boy" who shares their hobbies and interests and in the end, grows up to be a most respected religious and world leader.

### The Young Life of Mother Teresa of Calcutta

How Gonxha Agnes Bojaxhiu grew to be a world famous personage and a living example of Jesus in a dark world is the basis for this new book for young and old to treasure. This story gives insight into the people and events in Mother Teresa's young life that shaped the final woman — the early death of her beloved father, Nikola, a political figure in the days of unrest of

# Other Books continued

Yugoslavia; — her mother, the warm hospitable Dronda, who always had time for others. We learn how a "pretty mischievous young tomboy" eventually became a world revered "living saint."

### Give Me Jesus

A book that can be appreciated by any age, child or adult. It contains beautiful selections from authors past and present. It is a magical assortment of special prayers, reflections, and stories that focus on God's love for us. An inspiring tool in giving children building blocks to faith, as well as a trip down memory lane for their parents.

### Saint Maximilian Kolbe – The Story of the Two Crowns

St. Maximilian Kolbe is known throughout the world today for giving his life for another amid the horrors of the German concentration camp in World War II. Raymond's life as a young boy, the questions raised by the appearance of Mary, and all the events of his life leading to this crucial moment are touchingly recounted by the author in this inspiring story told through the eyes of the man saved from the "starvation bunker" in Auschwitz. An engaging story of a "not perfect" little boy.

All above available: Young Sparrow Press, P.O. Box 265, Worcester, PA 19490; (215) 997-0791

### The Young Life of Sister Faustina

This book follows young Helen along the courageous path of trust in our Lord. See God's plan begin to unfold even in the seemingly "ordinary" events of her childhood — First Communion, schoolwork, chores, and even fun. This is a book to help a child's faith. Helen is special — special in her calling, special in her response, and special in her mission of Divine Mercy. A delight to read.

Available: Marian Helpers, Stockbridge, MA 01263-0004; 1-800-462-7426